A Picnic Surprise!

Written by Amanda Cant
Illustrated by Ángeles Peinador

Activities

1 Read and match.

2 Find and count.

apples ⬜4⬜   biscuits ⬜ ⬜

sandwiches ⬜ ⬜   bananas ⬜ ⬜

Picture Dictionary

 sunny

 park

 tired

 kitchen

 picnic

 bored

 hungry

 apple

 banana

 biscuit

 sandwich

 living room

 camera

 photo

 football

 garden

 tortoise

 idea

 happy

 bag

Macmillan Education
4 Crinan Street
London N1 9XW
A division of Macmillan Publishers Limited
Companies and representatives throughout the world

ISBN 978 0 2300 1009 3
ISBN 978 0 2300 1008 6 (International Edition)

Text © Amanda Cant 2007
Design and illustration © Macmillan Publishers Limited 2007

First published 2007

All rights reserved; no part of this publication may be
reproduced, stored in a retrieval system, transmitted in any
form, or by any means, electronic, mechanical, photocopying,
recording, or otherwise, without the prior written permission of
the publishers.

Illustrated by Ángeles Peinador

Printed and bound in Brazil

2025
33